P9-EKE-836

RESISTANCE

BOOK 1

First Second

New York & London

Text Copyright © 2010 by Carla Jablonski
Illustrations Copyright © 2010 by Leland Purvis

Published by First Second
First Second is an imprint of Roaring Brook Press,
a division of Holtzbrinck Publishing Holdings Limited Partnership,
175 Fifth Avenue, New York, NY 10010

All rights reserved

Distributed in Canada by H. B. Fenn and Company Ltd.
distributed in the United Kingdom by Macmillan Children's Books,
a division of Pan Macmillan.

Design by Colleen AF Venable

Colored by Hilary Sycamore and Sky Blue Ink

Cataloging-in-Publication Data is on file at the Library of Congress.

ISBN: 978-1-59643-703-6

First Second books are available for special promotions and premiums.
For details, contact: Director of Special Markets, Holtzbrinck Publishers.

First Edition May 2010
Printed in June 2010 in China by C&C Joint Printing Co.,
Shenzhen, Guangdong Province
1 3 5 7 9 10 8 6 4 2

RESISTANCE
BOOK 1

Written by
Carla Jablonski

Art by
Leland Purvis

Color by
Hilary Sycamore

First Second

WORLD WAR II BEGAN ON SEPTEMBER 1, 1939, WITH THE INVASION OF POLAND BY NAZI GERMANY AND RUSSIA. BUT IT WAS NOT UNTIL 1940 THAT THE GERMANS INVADED FRANCE. THE FRENCH WERE FORCED TO SURRENDER WITHIN WEEKS.

ON JUNE 22, 1940, THE FRENCH AND THE GERMANS SIGNED AN ARMISTICE AGREEMENT. THE FRENCH WOULD STOP FIGHTING AND AGREE TO GERMAN DEMANDS. NOT EVEN A YEAR HAD PASSED SINCE FRANCE AND BRITAIN DECLARED WAR ON THE NAZIS. BUT FRANCE COULDN'T WIN AGAINST THE GERMAN ARMY.

FRANCE WAS DIVIDED INTO TWO ZONES: OCCUPIED, WHERE THE GERMANS WERE IN CHARGE, AND THE FREE, RUN BY THE NEW FRENCH GOVERNMENT, NOW IN VICHY.

THERE WERE MANY REASONS TO AGREE TO THIS PLAN. FRANCE WAS STILL RECOVERING FROM THE DEADLY BATTLES OF WORLD WAR I. IT SEEMED AS IF THE GERMANS WOULD WIN THIS SECOND WAR AND TO GIVE IN NOW, SOME BELIEVED, WOULD PROTECT FRANCE FOR THE FUTURE. ALSO, MANY OF THE FRENCH AGREED WITH NAZI IDEAS, OR WANTED A CHANGE IN GOVERNMENT, AND THERE WERE PEOPLE WHO TOOK ADVANTAGE OF THE CIRCUMSTANCES TO MAKE MONEY.

OCCUPIED

PARIS

•VICHY

"FREE"

BUT THERE WERE THOUSANDS (SOME SAY TENS OF THOUSANDS) OF FRENCH MEN, WOMEN AND EVEN CHILDREN WHO RESISTED IN WAYS LARGE AND SMALL FROM THE BEGINNING. THEY JOINED WELL-ORGANIZED NETWORKS OR SIMPLY ACTED ON THEIR OWN.

IN THE OCCUPIED ZONE, LIFE WAS SEVERELY RESTRICTED. CURFEWS, RATIONS, ROUND-UPS, ARRESTS, SEARCHES, AND EVEN TORTURE BECAME A WAY OF LIFE. THERE WERE GERMAN SOLDIERS EVERYWHERE. IN THE SOUTHERN "FREE" ZONE THERE WERE STILL SHORTAGES, STILL GERMANS PRESENT, BUT PEOPLE WERE NOT LIVING WITH THE SAME LEVEL OF FEAR AS THOSE NORTH OF THE DEMARCATION LINE. THEY WERE LIVING IN DEFEAT, BUT NOT LIVING UNDER OCCUPATION.

UNTIL 1942.

☦

1

3

5

7

10

TIME TO GO, **MARIE.**

DO I HAVE TO?

YOUR MAMA IS VERY LUCKY...

...TO HAVE SUCH A GOOD LITTLE WORKER TO HELP HER.

HOTÉL *Tessier*

TEST ME ON GEOGRAPHY?

MATH?

THAT NIGHT...

24

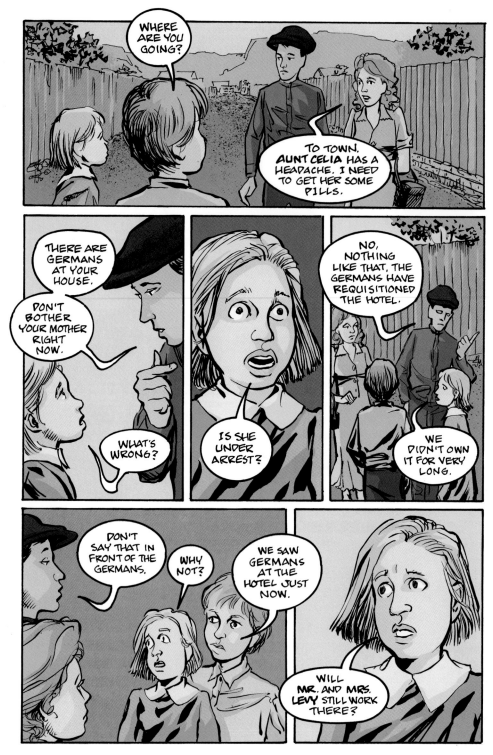

29

31

32

34

48

50

52

60

62

64

78

79

83

85

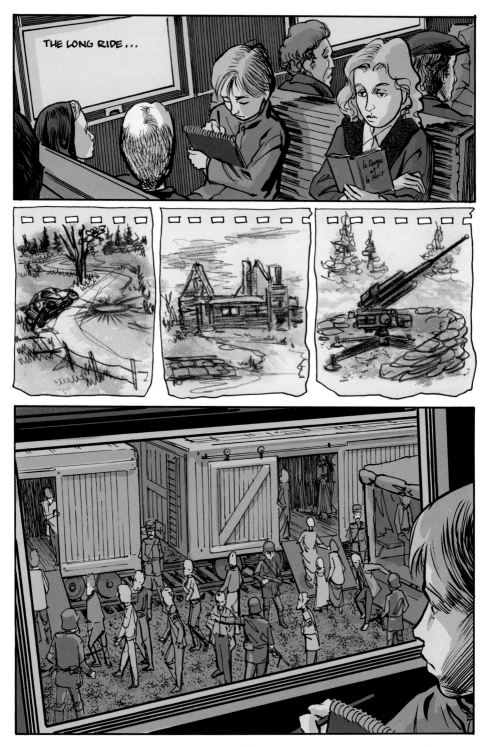

MY PARENTS— I COULD— THAT COULD BE—

PAPERS.

NO ONE SAID A WORD.

YOU!

HAND IT OVER.

118

119

——Author's Note——

There is no simple history of the Resistance in France during World War II. That's because resistance took many forms. There were well-organized secret paramilitary groups (who didn't always work together, and often disagreed about strategy); there were the Maquis, who were much more casually structured and often used guerrilla tactics; and finally, there were ordinary people who took action where they could to oppose the puppet Vichy government and the German occupiers.

This last group, perhaps, would be described as part of a resistance movement, rather than as members of "the Resistance." But all risked their lives, putting themselves—and perhaps others—in danger, and were crucial in the fight to liberate France.

Looking back, it may be easy to say that the only right action was to resist the German invaders, and to condemn those who didn't. But the definitions of who was a collaborator and who was a resistor are not so clear-cut. If a farmer made a big profit by selling to the Germans rather than to his hungry neighbors, he might have been considered a collaborator. After all, he was working with and helping the Germans. But this same farmer may also have been hiding forbidden radios, newspapers, or even Resistance fighters—putting his own life in danger.

And Resistance operatives, as brave as they were, weren't saints. They could be petty, vindictive, and sometimes used the Resistance as an excuse to steal or fight. Complicating things further, conditions in France were always changing. How French people felt and what they believed in 1940 were not necessarily the same in 1944.

History as written has a way of seeming clear, even inevitable. Yes, there may be different versions of "the truth," but there are definite winners and losers, friends and enemies, loyalties and betrayals.

History as lived is anything but clear! There is no way to watch the events unfold and make decisions based on somehow knowing what the outcome will be. Living history is messy, filled with missteps, confusion, mistakes, and choices made on the fly, in the moment, on the spot—with consequences that can be unpredictable and unintended.

Living in a country that has never been occupied, like the U.S., it is hard to imagine the pressures people faced. These pressures were both external (physical threats, lack of food, disappearing neighbors) and internal (fear, family loyalty, national pride, belief systems) and they influenced the choices people made. What seems obvious to us now was probably not at all obvious to anyone then.

If the Vichy government brought peace and saved lives, perhaps that wasn't such a terrible thing. If the British and the Americans bombed your town as they attacked German operations in your country, or demolished the roads they (and you) used, would you welcome them as heroes? If a daring sabotage of a train station by the Resistance resulted in the Germans taking revenge by executing forty townspeople, was it really a good move to make?

But what if you did nothing? How could you allow an invading army to take what you and your family owned, change your way of life, kill your friends, neighbors, and family members? Destroy everything you believed in, everything that mattered to you? What then?

Each French citizen, from the oldest great-grandmother to the youngest child, faced decisions like these on a daily basis. Each had their own story, their own personal concerns to weigh, risks to assess with no idea of how things would turn out, or even what the next day would bring. Sometimes those choices were regrettable, sometimes noble. All were difficult.